# SKY RIDER

## ANDY AND ANGIE BELCHER

LEARNING
MEDIA®

Distributed in the United States of America by Pacific Learning,
P. O. Box 2723, Huntington Beach, CA 92647-0723
Web site: www.pacificlearning.com

Published 1999 by Learning Media Limited,
Box 3293, Wellington 6001, New Zealand
Web site: www.learningmedia.com

10 9 8 7 6 5 4 3

Printed in Hong Kong

ISBN 0 478 22949 6

PL 9314

I looked out of the plane door. Far below, the earth was spread out like a patchwork quilt.

"Jump run!" the pilot called.

I pulled my goggles down over my eyes and moved forward. The wind pulled at my hair and face. Down below, I could see the runway. That was my target.

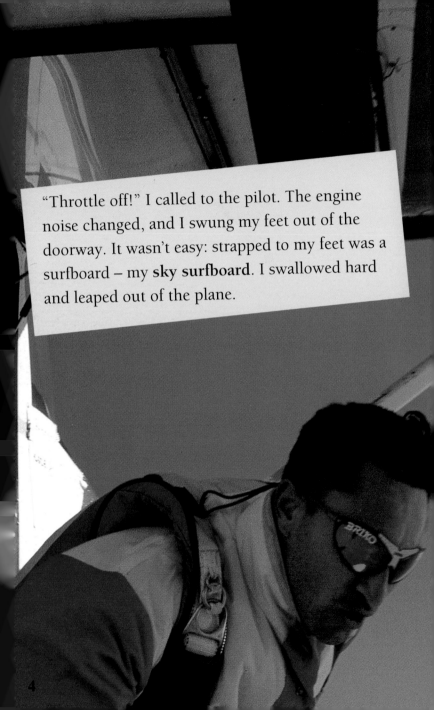

"Throttle off!" I called to the pilot. The engine noise changed, and I swung my feet out of the doorway. It wasn't easy: strapped to my feet was a surfboard – my **sky surfboard**. I swallowed hard and leaped out of the plane.

The wind pulled even harder. It pulled at my clothing and my body. And it pulled at the board, making me twist around and around, head over heels at 160 miles an hour. But something was wrong. This wasn't how I thought it would be.

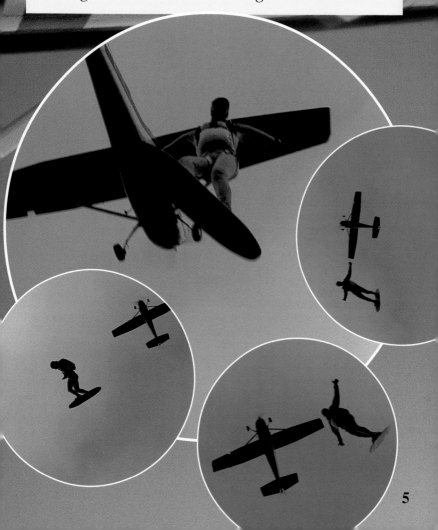

The ground was a blur. I knew that if I didn't release the surfboard and my **pilot chute** quickly, I might black out. I tugged at a cord, and the surfboard fell off my feet. I pulled the pilot chute out of its pocket. It caught the wind and dragged out the main chute.

My body was suddenly jerked upright, and I floated to the ground.

I've been skydiving for twelve
years – more than two thousand jumps – but that
was the first time I'd tried sky surfing. The videos
I'd watched had made it look easy and exciting.
Standing up and riding the sky waves had
sounded so cool. I'm much better at it now, but
that first surf was not what I'd expected.

# Chapter 2

Skydiving is a dangerous sport if you're not prepared. Before each jump, I take my time to prepare and check my equipment.

First I pack my chute. I check the **lines** and carefully fold the **canopy**.

I squash the chute up small and pack it into the container. The container has flaps like an envelope, held together with a strong steel pin.

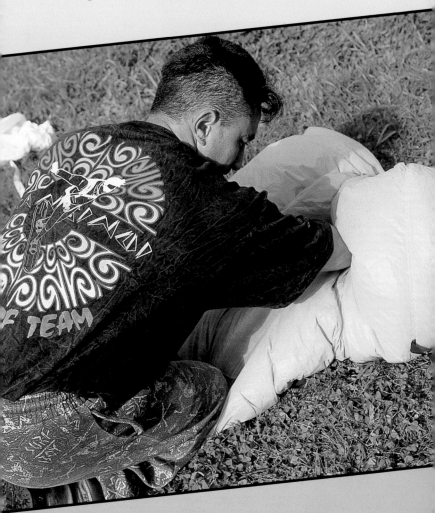

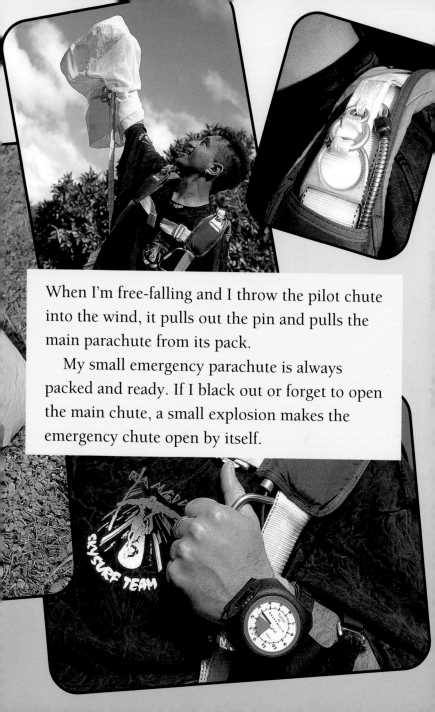

When I'm free-falling and I throw the pilot chute into the wind, it pulls out the pin and pulls the main parachute from its pack.

My small emergency parachute is always packed and ready. If I black out or forget to open the main chute, a small explosion makes the emergency chute open by itself.

Then I pack my **jumpsuit**, my **webbed gloves**, and an **altimeter**. The altimeter is like a small clock that tells me how high up in the air I am. An alarm on the altimeter will warn me if I get too close to the ground.

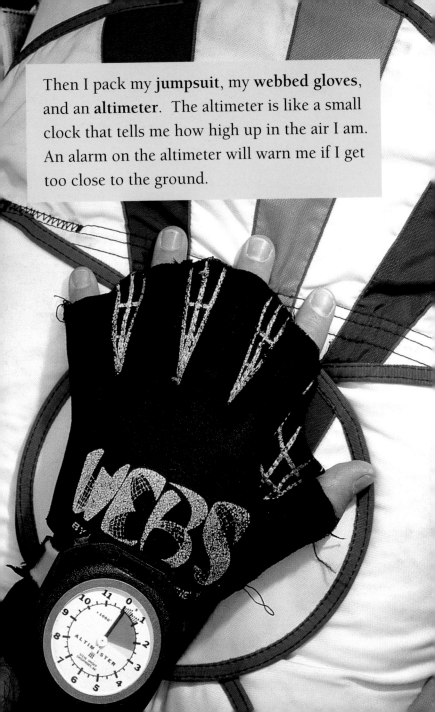

I check the sky surfboard last. It has a set of
bindings to hold it in place on my feet. There's a
**quick-release cord** connected to the bindings so
that I can drop the board just before I land.

When I feel sure I have everything, I head for the **drop zone**. There is always a lot of excitement at the airport hangar. Today, a trainee skydiver is practicing her countdown drill before going up for her first jump. Hopefully, she won't land in a tree like I did my first time.

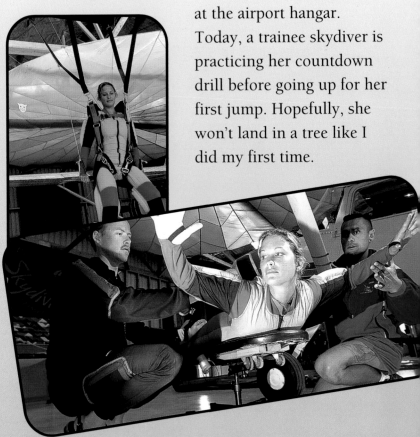

Not many try sky surfing. When I arrive, there's a feeling that something different and exciting is going to happen.

# Chapter 3

The plane sits waiting for
the jumpers. The pilot tells me that the weather
looks good – just a slight breeze and a few tiny
puffs of cloud. "Hey, you're not afraid of a little
puff of cloud, are you?" he jokes.

Clouds look harmless enough, but I don't like surfing through them. It's hard to know which way you're going. It's like being lost in a thick fog. Once I was upside down, and I didn't even know it! Clouds fog up your goggles, and you can't read your altimeter. It's scary.

I keep going up and jumping all through the day. The higher the plane flies, the more air time I have to try something new. Every jump is different. It's like a battle between me and the board. The air pushes it in one direction, and I try to make it go in another. It's not like surfing in the sea, where you can see the waves. This sea is invisible.

But the great thing with sky surfing is that you can turn around and look at everything. The earth is spread beneath you like a great, green pancake.

I try different boards, different jumpsuits, and even different parachutes. I know that "practice makes perfect," and I want to be at the next world championships.

# Chapter 4

Sometimes I go up with my friend Greg. He's a free-fall photographer. He loves to take photographs of other skydivers as they zoom past in the sky. Together, Greg and I make up a sky surfing competition team.

A sky surfing competition team has to have two skydivers – a sky surfer and a camera operator. The sky surfer makes the moves on his board, and the camera operator films them. There are two cameras on Greg's helmet. His helmet is very, very heavy.

He works the video camera with a control he has in his hand. The other, a "stills" camera, has a cable with its end in Greg's mouth. He presses a small button with his tongue to take the photos! Judges look at the videotape and then give the sky surfer and the camera operator a score.

While the plane is still on the ground, Greg and I practice getting in and out of it. This is called a "dirt dive." And I need the practice – it's hard to jump out of a plane with a surfboard strapped to your feet.

We talk about the moves I'll make. It's too noisy to talk in the plane, and when you're falling through the sky, the wind is so loud that it's hard to hear anything else.

This practice time is when I get scared.

# Chapter 5

As the plane speeds along the runway, the butterflies start in my stomach. I check my gear again. Main chute – check; emergency chute – check; altimeter alarm set – check; surfboard bindings – check ….

The plane circles as it climbs – six thousand feet, nine thousand feet, twelve thousand feet. The houses, farms, and cars are looking smaller and smaller. I put my head out of the door to see where the airfield is. That cold wind whips my face. My eyes sting, and my nose starts to run.

My heart beats faster.

"Jump run!" the pilot calls.

Greg is the first out. Carefully he crawls along the wing strut. He hangs on tight. I swing my legs out of the doorway and wriggle to the very edge. We look at each other. "Ready?"

"Ready," says Greg.

"Three, two, one, go!" we call together.

The air pushes against the surfboard, sending me out of control. The ground turns around and around. There's no time to be scared now. Something is wrong, and I have to act quickly. I drop the board and open the main parachute.

"What went wrong?" Greg asks when we're back on the ground.

"I'm not sure," I say. "Maybe I need to try my other board."

"Well, there's only one thing to do," Greg says. "Jump again!"

We repack the chutes, practice the dirt dives, and climb back onto the plane.

# Chapter 6

As the plane approaches jump run, we both check our gear. The pilot throttles off. A few puffs of cloud skim past the door. Greg crawls out onto the wing again and waits. Then comes the countdown … and the jump!

I try to think about what I'm doing. I push my feet hard against the board. At last! I'm in control and the right way up! The skyboard skims across the world. I stretch my arms wide and spread my fingers in the gloves. If I change position, I can do forward rolls, back loops, flips, and spins. The gloves are like rudders that help me to turn.

Greg flies around me taking photos. He is careful not to get in my way. We're moving at more than 130 miles an hour. We don't want to crash into each other. Then Greg moves away and opens his pilot chute. I can't resist one more quick spin.

The gentle ride down is quite different from the excitement of riding the sky waves. As the ground moves closer, I drop the board. I land gently, and the canopy falls quietly behind me.

I let out an almighty "Yahoo!" and scoop up the chute.

It's time to repack and then surf the sky again!